page 6-7

page 8

page 12

page 14

page 16

page 18-19

page 29

Leap Ahead

Leap Ahead Workbook

English

Home learning made fun

Cat

Frog

Dog

igloobooks

This is Me!

Draw a picture of yourself:

Write your name:

PARENT TIP: Your child might find it difficult to hold a pencil at this age. However, they will love trying to write their own name, even if it is simply to make letter-like marks. It's a great way to start writing!

Sounds All Around

Look at each picture. What sound does it make? Can you make the sound **LOUDLY** and quietly?

PARENT TIP: Encouraging your child to listen and repeat everyday sounds is good preparation for the phonics that they will learn in school. Ask them to listen for different sounds when you are out and about.

3

Pet Pairs

Look carefully at the shapes to see which ones match. Draw a line between each pair.

(a)

(1)

(b)

(2)

(c)

(3)

(d)

(4)

Answers on page 32

Animal Patterns

Look carefully at these animal pairs and circle the odd one out in each row.

 a

 b

 c

 d

 e

Answers on page 32

PARENT TIP: Matching outlines and patterns is a great way to prepare a child for identifying letter shapes. Encourage them to focus on the similarities and details of patterns and shapes.

It's Time to Rhyme!

Look at the pictures in each row and say the words. Then find the items on your sticker sheet whose names rhyme with the words in each row.

1 frog   log   dog

2 cat   bat

3   coat   goat

Answers on page 32

④ wig · dig

⑤ · sing · sting

⑥ ham · lamb

⑦ claw · · paw

Over the Moon

Follow the arrows to draw around these planets. Can you find some spaceship stickers on your sticker sheet to land on them?

8

Space Message

Ace the Alien has been learning about letters. Help him by following the arrows to make these letter shapes.

PARENT TIP: All these letters are made using round shapes, like the planets on the opposite page.

9

Odd Rhyme Out

Look at the pictures in each row and say the words out loud. Colour the two words that rhyme in blue. Colour the word that doesn't rhyme in red.

hand   sand   sheep

① ②

PARENT TIP: Your child might need to practise before they can hear words which rhyme. Help them to hear rhyming sounds by saying, "I've got a spoon. What can you see that sounds like spoon?"

Farmer Fred's Fence

Follow the arrows and finish the fence to help Farmer Fred. Then add some sheep stickers from your sticker sheet.

Now follow the arrows to practise writing these letters.

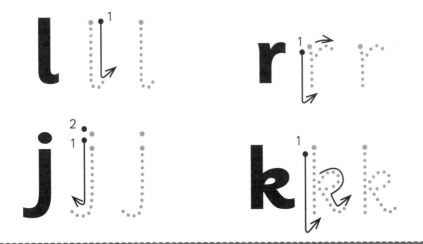

'a' and 's' Words

Colour the items that start with 'a' in red.
Colour the items that start with 's' in blue.
Two items have been coloured for you.

robot

sunglasses

carrot

sock

a

duck

ant

arrow

cat

s

apple

chair

cow

sack

Answers on page 32

PARENT TIP: Help your child to say the sound made by each letter,
e.g. 'a' for 'apple', 's' for 'sock'. Then, sound-talk the names of each item.

13

Ocean I Spy

Play I Spy with this ocean scene and see how many items you can spot. For example, 'I spy with my little eye, something beginning with... d.'

PARENT TIP: When you play 'I Spy', take care how you say the first sound in each word ("sss" not "suh", for example). Take it in turns to choose a letter and guess the answer. Don't worry if your child says the wrong answer. Give them lots of praise for trying.

Add some sea stickers from your sticker sheet

All at Sea

It's a nice day out at sea. Follow the arrows to draw some waves around the fishing boat, then add some seagull stickers in the sky.

Now follow the arrows to practise writing these letters.

't' and 'p' Words

Colour the items that start with 't' in red.
Colour the items that start with 'p' in blue.
Two items have been coloured for you.

penguin

pen

bed

glove

t

train

dog

tent

bird

ring

p

sock

10 ten

pig

Answers on page 32

Same Sound Stickers

Look at the pictures and say the words out loud. Find a sticker for something that starts with the same sound as the rest of the things in each row. The first one has been done for you.

1. sock   sack   sand

2. tap   ten

3. nest   neck

4. bed   bag

4

apple ant

5

gate garden

6

cat cot

7

dog desk

Lily Pad Letters

Look at these happy frogs. Follow the arrows to draw the shape they make as they hop from one lily pad to the next.

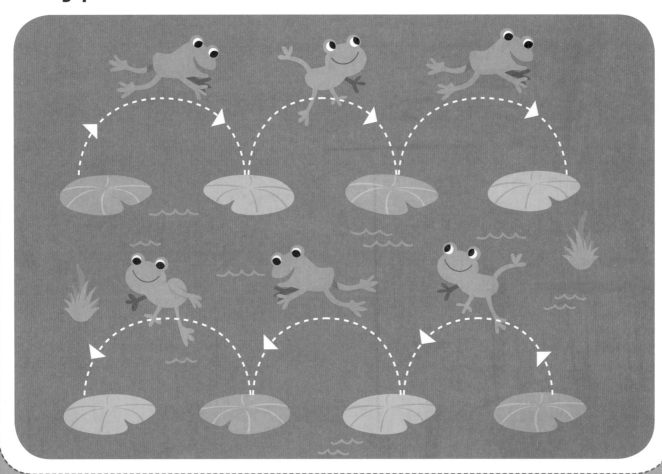

Now follow the arrows to practise writing these letters.

'n' and 'm' Words

Colour the items that start with 'n' in red.
Colour the items that start with 'm' in blue.
Two items have been coloured for you.

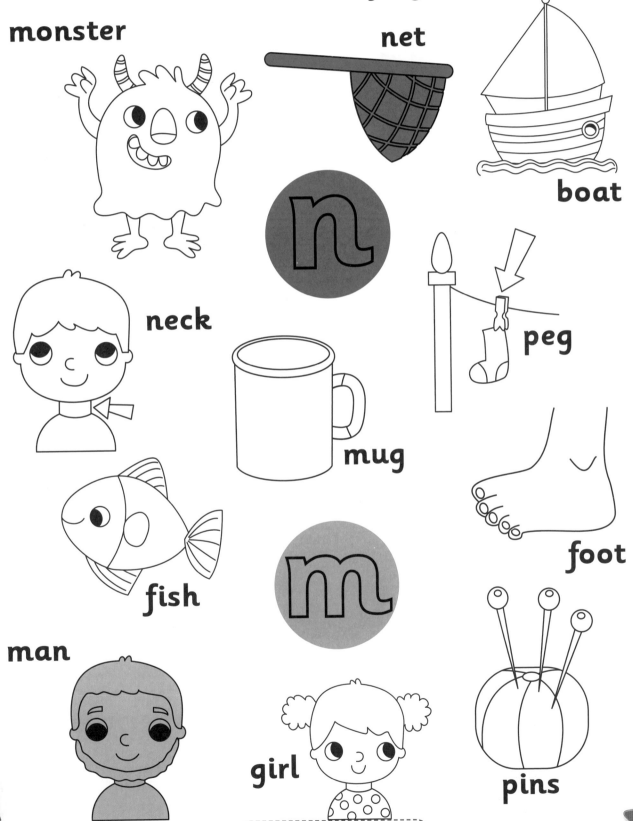

monster

net

boat

n

neck

mug

peg

fish

m

foot

man

girl

pins

Answers on page 32

Odd Toy Out

These toys have letters on them, but the odd letters keep getting in the way! Circle the odd letter out in each row.

1. s s s t s
2. m n m m m
3. o p p p p
4. g g r g g

Answers on page 32

22

Silly Sentences

Read the beginning of each silly sentence out loud.
What silly word will you put at the end?
Use the pictures to help.

 Simon Sailor's sack is full of ....

snails   sand   slugs

 Wispy Witch wishes for a ....

wand   wasp   walrus

 Millie Mouse makes a mess with ....

mud   mittens   moles

 Billie Baker bakes ....

biscuits   bugs   beds

PARENT TIP: You and your child can have fun making up your own sentences together. It's a great way to pass the time and encourage children to think creatively.

23

Zigzag Robots

Sammy Science has almost finished his robots. Help him to complete them by following the zigzag lines.

Now follow the arrows to practise writing these letters.

'd' and 'g' Words

Colour the items that start with 'd' in red.
Colour the items that start with 'g' in blue.
Two items have been coloured for you.

dragon

hat

heart

garden

d

gate

goat

rabbit

cap

bed

g

dog

duck

star

Answers on page 32

Rhyming I Spy

Look at the park scene and use these pictures to play Rhyming I Spy. For example, "I spy with my little eye, something that rhymes with... balloon."

balloon   hand   clock   cot   hat   log   mop   wig

What's the Picture?

There's a shape hidden in the grid below. Colour the 'c' squares red and the 'k' squares yellow to find out what it is.

k	c	c	c	k	c	c	c	k
c	c	c	c	c	c	c	c	c
k	c	c	c	c	c	c	c	k
k	k	c	c	c	c	c	k	k
k	k	k	c	c	c	k	k	k
k	k	k	k	c	k	k	k	k
k	k	k	k	k	k	k	k	k

Answer on page 32

Aladdin's Magic Lamp

How many things in the cave can you find beginning with each of these sounds?

b	h	f	r

Hidden in the cave is Aladdin's magic lamp. When you find it, place the genie sticker from your sticker sheet by the lamp.

Me and My Sounds

What letter does your name start with?

Draw a picture of something that starts with the same sound as your name:

Draw a picture of you and your best friend:

What letter does your best friend's name start with?

Answers

Page 4: Pet Pairs
a – 3, b – 4, c – 2, d – 1

Page 5: Animal Patterns

a

b

c

d

e

Pages 6–7: It's Time to Rhyme!

dog, hat, boat, pig, wing, jam, saw

Page 13: 'a' and 's' Words
'a': arrow, apple, ant
's': sunglasses, sock, sack

Page 17: 't' and 'p' Words
't': tent, train, ten
'p': pen, penguin, pig

Page 21: 'n' and 'm' Words
'n': net, neck
'm': man, monster, mug

Page 22: Odd Toy Out

1   2   3   4

Page 25: 'd' and 'g' Words
'd': dog, dragon, duck
'g': garden, goat, gate

Page 28: What's the Picture? A heart.